Make it easy...

English

Quick Tests

Age 5-6

Louis Fidge

Test 1 The alphabet

All **words** are made up of **letters**. There are **26** letters in the **alphabet**.

Fill in the missing letters.

a b **1.**__ d e f
j **3.**__ h **2.**__
k l **4.**__ n
o
5.__
r q
6.__ **10.**__
7.__
u
8.__ w **9.**__ y

10
9
8
7
6
5
4
3
2
1

Colour in your score

Test 2 Making some words (1)

The sound of the **first letter** of each of these words is the **same**.

sun   saw   sink

Choose one of these letters to start each word.

m   p   h

1. ____eg

2. ____an

3. ____op

4. ____in

5. ____at

6. ____ut

7. ____en

8. ____op

9. ____ug

10. ____en

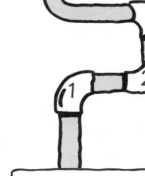

10
9 8
7
6
5
4
3
2
1

Colour in your score

Test 2

Test 3 Making some words (2)

We use **letters** to make **words**.

b + a + t = bat

Do these sums. Write the words you make.

1. s + a + d = _____

2. d + i + g = _____

3. b + a + g = _____

4. t + o + p = _____

5. l + e + g = _____

6. f + o + x = _____

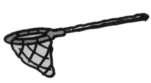

7. n + e + t = _____

8. t + u + b = _____

9. d + o + g = _____

10. j + u + g = _____

Colour in your score

Test 3

Test 4 **Labels**

Many pictures have **labels** to help you.

Write the correct name under each animal.

| monkey | goat | horse | tiger | kangaroo |
| donkey | bear | zebra | camel | panda |

1. _____   2. _____   3. _____

4. _____   5. _____   6. _____

7. _____   8. _____

9. _____

10. _____

Colour in your score

Test 4

Test 5 Sentences

A **sentence** must make **sense**.

I to hop like. ☒   I like to hop. ☑

Write the words in order to make some sentences.

1. sun yellow. The is _____

2. green. is grass The _____

3. read. like to I _____

4. lay eggs. Hens _____

5. lion A roar. can _____

6. raining. is It _____

7. in You water. swim _____

8. ball. You a kick _____

9. door The shut. is _____

10. stripes. A has tiger _____

10
9
8
7
6
5
4
3
2
1

Colour in your score

Test 5

Test 6 Missing words

A **sentence** must make **sense**.

ROAR

A roars. ☒   A lion roars. ☑

Choose the best word to finish each sentence.

elephant	sun	money	cup	kangaroo
banana	star	spade	bike	umbrella

1. You ride a _____.

2. The _____ shines.

3. A _____ twinkles.

4. You spend _____.

5. You eat a _____.

6. A _____ hops.

7. You need an _____ in the rain.

8. You drink from a _____.

9. An _____ has a trunk.

10. You dig with a _____.

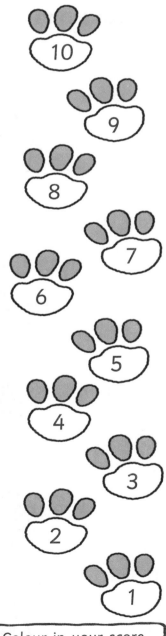

Colour in your score

Test 6

Test 7 Last letters

The sound of the **last letter** of each of these words is the **same**.

pen   pin   pan

Choose one of these letters to finish each word.

t   g   p

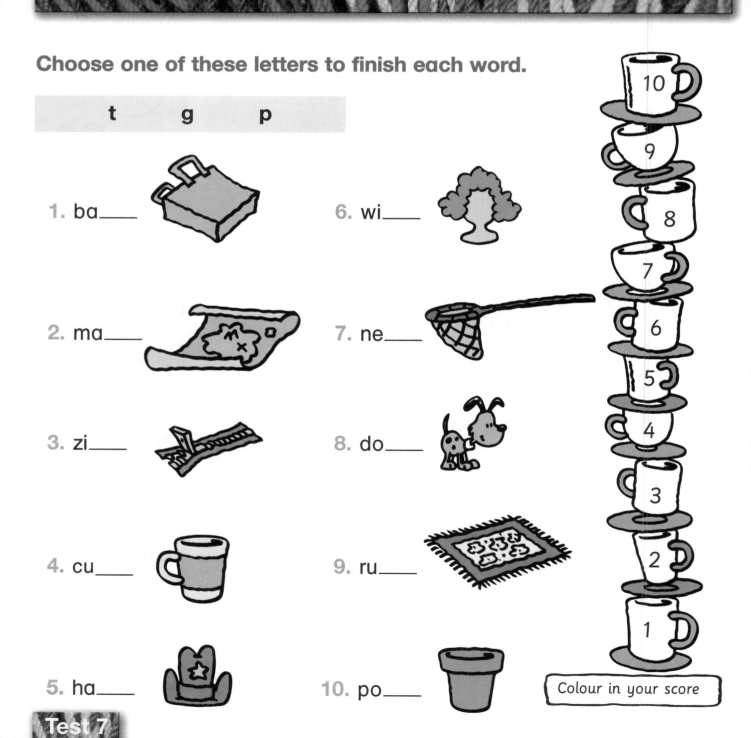

1. ba____

2. ma____

3. zi____

4. cu____

5. ha____

6. wi____

7. ne____

8. do____

9. ru____

10. po____

Colour in your score

Test 7

Test 8 Groups of words

We sometimes **group** words together. These are all **birds**.

hen   parrot   sparrow

bike   rocket   helicopter   bus   aeroplane

boat   yacht   car   ship   lorry

Sort these things into groups.

Things that go on land.

1. _____	3. _____
2. _____	4. _____

Things that fly in the sky.   Things that go on the water.

5. _____	8. _____
6. _____	9. _____
7. _____	10. _____

10
9
8
7
6
5
4
3
2
1

Colour in your score

Test 8

Test 9 **Word building**

We can **build** words from **letters** and **groups of letters**.

b + ag   r + ag   w + ag

bag   rag   wag

Do these sums. Write the words you make.

1. f + an = _____

2. s + ix = _____

3. v + an = _____

4. n + od = _____

5. l + eg = _____

6. r + od = _____

7. p + eg = _____

8. c + ut = _____

9. m + ix = _____

10. n + ut = _____

10
9
8
7
6
5
4
3
2
1

Colour in your score

Test 9

Test 10 Middle letters

The sound of the **middle letter** of each of these words is the **same**.

pan   bat   bag

Choose the correct middle letter to make each word.

a	o	o	i
1. j___m		6. s___b	
u	a	i	e
2. t___p		7. t___n	
u	o	e	i
3. l___g		8. t___n	
o	u	a	i
4. b___n		9. b___b	
u	e	e	a
5. t___b		10. j___t	

Colour in your score

Test 10

Test 11 Capital letters and full stops

A **sentence** always begins with a **capital letter** and often ends with a **full stop**.

The girl fell off her bike!

Write these sentences correctly.

1. the rain falls _____

2. a tree grows tall _____

3. the sky is blue _____

4. my cup is full _____

5. a cow moos _____

6. we like books _____

7. you bang a drum _____

8. it is sunny _____

9. a ball is round _____

10. i like to sing _____

10
9
8
7
6
5
4
3
2
1

Colour in your score

Test 12 The letters ff, ll and ss

Some words end with **double letters**.

Pass the ball.

	doll	off	bell	
hill	toss		puff	fall
	hiss	cuff	fuss	

Write the words that end with ff.

1. _____   3. _____

2. _____

Write the words that end with ll.

4. _____   6. _____

5. _____   7. _____

Write the words that end with ss.

8. _____   10. _____

9. _____

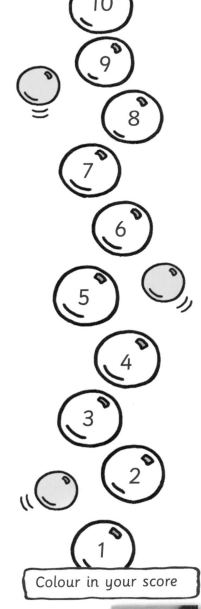

Colour in your score

Test 12

Test 13 The letters ck

Many words end in **ck**.

A du**ck** says qua**ck**.

Do these sums. Write the words you make.

1. b + a + ck = _____

2. p + a + ck = _____

3. n + e + ck = _____

4. p + e + ck = _____

5. k + i + ck = _____

6. s + i + ck = _____

7. l + o + ck = _____

8. d + o + ck = _____

9. l + u + ck = _____

10. s + u + ck = _____

10
9
8
7
6
5
4
3
2
1

Colour in your score

Test 13

Test 14 The letters ng and nk

Many words end in **ng** and **nk**.

I can si**ng**.

I can thi**nk**.

Find and write the ng or nk words that are hiding.

1. a b a n g w   _bang_

2. b a n k t y   _____

3. h g k i n g   _____

4. b s o n g m   _____

5. f v s a n k   _____

6. h a n g j b   _____

7. s a r i n g   _____

8. z l i n k n   _____

9. b u n k x c   _____

10. j h p i n k   _____

10

9

8

7

6

5

4

3

2

1

Colour in your score

Test 14

Test 15 Letter blends at the beginning of words

These words all have **l** as a second letter.

slide   fly   clock   black   glue

Write the new words you make.

1. Change the **fl** in **fl**ip to **sl**.   _slip_

2. Change the **pl** in **pl**ot to **sl**.   _____

3. Change the **sl** in **sl**at to **fl**.   _____

4. Change the **cl** in **cl**ick to **fl**.   _____

5. Change the **fl** in **fl**ap to **cl**.   _____

6. Change the **bl** in **bl**ink to **cl**.   _____

7. Change the **cl** in **cl**ot to **bl**.   _____

8. Change the **sl** in **sl**ack to **bl**.   _____

9. Change the **cl** in **cl**ass to **gl**.   _____

10. Change the **cl** in **cl**ad to **gl**.   _____

10
9
8
7
6
5
4
3
2
1

Colour in your score

Test 16 Letter blends at the end of words

Say these words slowly. Listen to the way they **end**.

bolt   she**lf**   mi**lk**   he**lp**   go**ld**

	hold	elf	milk	
yelp	belt	silk	gold	
	help	shelf	melt	

Write the pairs of rhyming words.

Write the words that end with ld.

1. _____ 2. _____

Write the words that end with lf.

3. _____ 4. _____

Write the words that end with lk.

5. _____ 6. _____

Write the words that end with lp.

7. _____ 8. _____

Write the words that end with lt.

9. _____ 10. _____

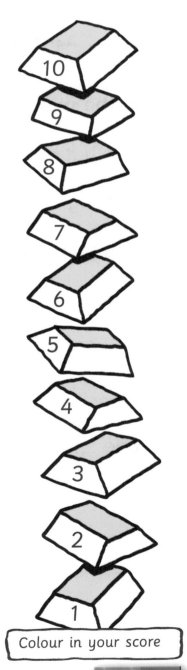

Colour in your score

Test 16

Test 17 Plurals

Plural means when there is **more than one**.

We add **s** to many words to make them plural.

one rabbit　　　　　three rabbits

Fill in the missing word.

1. one hat but two _____.

2. one leg but two _____.

3. one tin but two _____.

4. one pot but two _____.

5. one mug but two _____.

6. one _____ but two pans.

7. one _____ but two pets.

8. one _____ but two lips.

9. one _____ but two dogs.

10. one _____ but two sums.

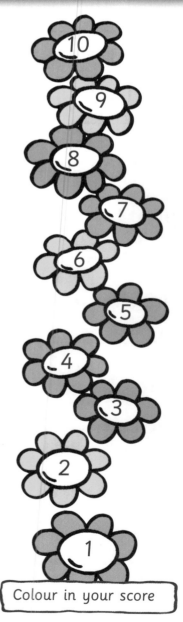

Colour in your score

Test 17

Test 18 Sets of words

This is a **set** of fruit.

orange banana apple

This is a **set** of animals.

lion   monkey   elephant

potato   butterfly cabbage onion   ant

carrot   beetle cauliflower earwig   turnip

Write the names of the vegetables.

1. _____   4. _____

2. _____   5. _____

3. _____   6. _____

Write the names of the insects.

7. _____   9. _____

8. _____   10. _____

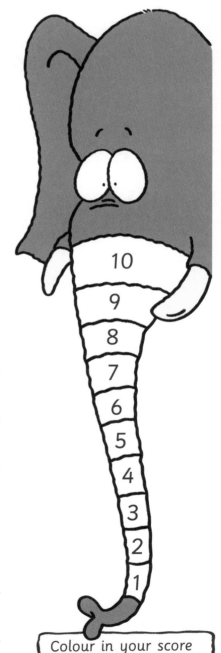

10
9
8
7
6
5
4
3
2
1

Colour in your score

Test 18

Test 19 Silly sentences

A **sentence** must make **sense**.

The dog ate the bone. ☑   The bone ate the dog. ☒

Write each sentence correctly.

1. A cow barks.   _____

2. A dog moos.   _____

3. A duck hisses.   _____

4. A horse cheeps.   _____

5. A hen neighs.   _____

6. A sheep chirps.   _____

7. A snake quacks.   _____

8. A bird bleats.   _____

9. A bee brays.   _____

10. A donkey buzzes._____

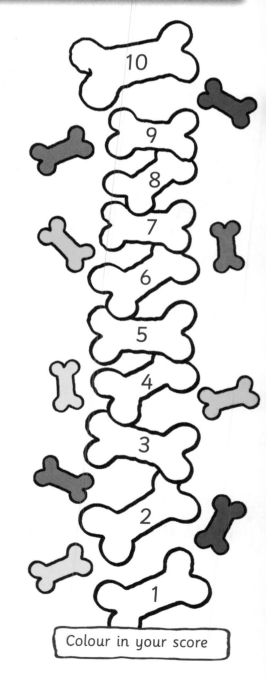

10
9
8
7
6
5
4
3
2
1

Colour in your score

Test 19

Test 20 The letters sh and ch

You will find **sh** and **ch** in many words.

*fi**sh** and **ch**ips*

Choose sh or ch to complete each word.

1. _____est

2. _____ell

3. _____ip

4. di_____

5. _____eep

6. ben_____

7. _____icken

8. tor_____

9. _____eese

10. bru_____

10
9
8
7
6
5
4
3
2
1

Colour in your score

Test 20

Test 21 The letters ee and oo

The letters **ee** and **oo** are two common letter patterns.

*I have some b**oo**ts on my f**ee**t.*

Choose ee or oo to complete each word.

1. _____l

2. st_____l

3. p_____l

4. br_____m

5. m_____n

6. tr_____

7. w_____p

8. f_____d

9. sw_____t

10. b_____

Colour in your score

Test 22 The letters ay and ai

The letters **ay** often come at the **end** of a word.

The letters **ai** often come in the **middle** of a word.

tr**ay**

tr**ai**n

Choose ai or ay to complete the word in each sentence.

1. It is a lovely d_____.

2. The r_____n is falling.

3. I hit the n_____l with a hammer.

4. You can swim in the b_____.

5. You can make things with cl_____.

6. The sn_____l went slowly.

7. I had to w_____t for my dinner.

8. You can pl_____ in the park.

9. The plates are on a tr_____.

10. You will have to w_____t and see.

10
9
8
7
6
5
4
3
2
1

Colour in your score

Test 22

Test 23 Vowels and consonants

There are **26** letters in the **alphabet**.

a	b	c	d	e	f	g	h	i	j	k	l	m
n	o	p	q	r	s	t	u	v	w	x	y	z

The five **vowels** are **a, e, i, o, u**.

All the other letters are called **consonants**.

Fill in the missing vowel in each word.

1. m___t

2. s___n

3. b___d

4. n___t

5. b___b

6. b___g

7. f___x

8. s___x

9. m___d

10. b___n

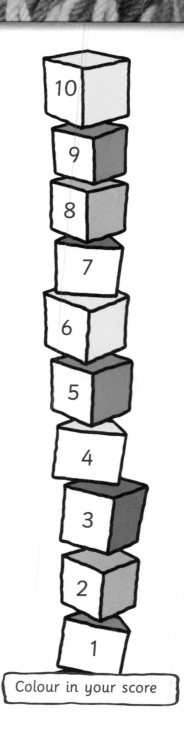

10
9
8
7
6
5
4
3
2
1

Colour in your score

Test 24 Names

Whenever we write **someone's name** we should always **start** with a **capital letter**.

Humpty Dumpty sat on a wall.

Write the names of these nursery rhyme characters correctly.

1. humpty dumpty _____

2. little bo peep _____

3. margery daw _____

4. tommy tucker _____

5. jack horner _____

6. polly _____

7. mary _____

8. lucy locket _____

9. georgie porgie _____

10. bobby shafto _____

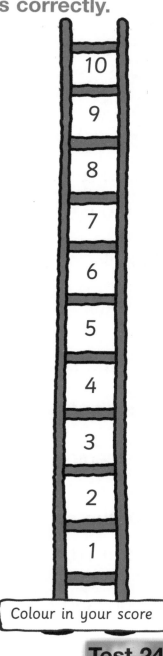

10

9

8

7

6

5

4

3

2

1

Colour in your score

Test 24

Test 25 The endings ing and ed

We can add **ing** and **ed** to the ends of some words.

I am wash**ing** my face.
wash + ing = washing

Yesterday I wash**ed** my feet.
wash + ed = washed

Add ing to each word. Write the word you make.

1. talk _____

2. lick _____

3. draw _____

Add ed to each word. Write the word you make.

4. shout _____

5. kick _____

6. crawl _____

Take the ing off. Write the word you are left with.

7. sniffing _____

8. sleeping _____

Take the ed off. Write the word you are left with.

9. turned _____

10. passed _____

Colour in your score

Test 25

Test 26 Questions

A question must begin with a **capital letter** and end with a **question mark**.

capital letter

question mark

How many legs has a spider?

Write these questions correctly.

1. what is for tea

_____

2. when are you coming

_____

3. what shape is a ball

_____

4. who is making that noise

_____

5. where do you live

_____

6. how many sweets have you got

_____

7. what is your address

_____

8. who is your teacher

_____

9. when is it time for dinner

_____

10. where is London

_____

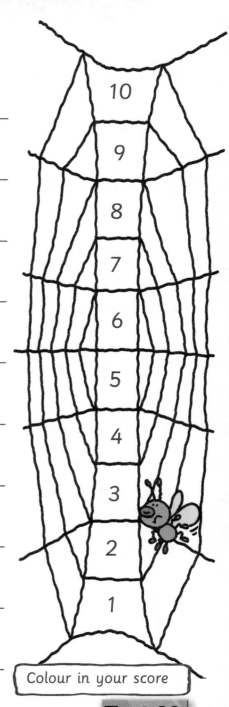

Colour in your score

Test 26

Test 27 The letters ea and oa

The two letter patterns **ea** and **oa** are common.

*a b**oa**t on the s**ea***

Write the new words you make.

1. Change the **s** in **sea** to **t**. _____

2. Change the **b** in **beat** to **s**. _____

3. Change the **l** in **leap** to **h**. _____

4. Change the **b** in **beak** to **l**. _____

5. Change the **t** in **teach** to **b**. _____

6. Change the **g** in **goat** to **b**. _____

7. Change the **f** in **foal** to **g**. _____

8. Change the **t** in **toad** to **r**. _____

9. Change the **c** in **coast** to **t**. _____

10. Change the **p** in **poach** to **c**. _____

10

9

8

7

6

5

4

3

2

1

Colour in your score

Test 27

Test 28 Magic e

Look what happens when we add **e** to the **end** of some words.

hop + e = hope

Do these sums. Write the words you make.

1. mad + e = _____

2. slid + e = _____

3. mak + e = _____

4. can + e = _____

5. cub + e = _____

6. rob + e = _____

7. shin + e = _____

8. cut + e = _____

9. tap + e = _____

10. bit + e = _____

Colour in your score

Test 28

Test 29 The months of the year

It is important to know how to spell the **months of the year** correctly.

Here are the months of the year in the wrong order.

August	May	December	January
February	June	October	March
September	April	November	July

Fill in the missing months in order. Spell them correctly.

January

February

1. _____

2. _____

3. _____

4. _____

5. _____

6. _____

7. _____

8. _____

9. _____

10. _____

Colour in your score

Test 30 Rhyming

Rhyming is important in spelling.

A plane can **fly** in the **sky**.

	ring	bake	train	
goat	cool		king	coat
	chain	pool	cake	

Write the pairs of rhyming words.

Write the ing words.

1. _____

2. _____

Write the ain words.

7. _____

8. _____

Write the ool words.

3. _____

4. _____

Write the ake words.

9. _____

10. _____

Write the oat words.

5. _____

6. _____

Colour in your score

Test 30

ANSWERS

Test 1
1. c   6. s
2. g   7. t
3. i   8. v
4. m   9. x
5. p   10. z

Test 2
1. peg
2. pan
3. hop
4. pin
5. mat
6. hut
7. hen
8. mop
9. mug
10. pen

Test 3
1. sad
2. dig
3. bag
4. top
5. leg
6. fox
7. net
8. tub
9. dog
10. jug

Test 4
1. camel
2. horse
3. kangaroo
4. zebra
5. bear
6. tiger
7. monkey
8. goat
9. donkey
10. panda

Test 5
1. The sun is yellow.
2. The grass is green.
3. I like to read.
4. Hens lay eggs.
5. A lion can roar.
6. It is raining.
7. You swim in water.
8. You kick a ball.
9. The door is shut.
10. A tiger has stripes.

Test 6
1. bike
2. sun
3. star
4. money
5. banana
6. kangaroo
7. umbrella
8. cup
9. elephant
10. spade

Test 7
1. bag
2. map
3. zip
4. cup
5. hat
6. wig
7. net
8. dog
9. rug
10. pot

Test 8
1. bike
2. bus
3. car
4. lorry
5. rocket
6. helicopter
7. aeroplane
8. boat
9. yacht
10. ship

Test 9
1. fan
2. six
3. van
4. nod
5. leg
6. rod
7. peg
8. cut
9. mix
10. nut

Test 10
1. jam
2. tap
3. log
4. bun
5. tub
6. sob
7. ten
8. tin
9. bib
10. jet

Test 11
1. The rain falls.
2. A tree grows tall.
3. The sky is blue.
4. My cup is full.
5. A cow moos.
6. We like books.
7. You bang a drum.
8. It is sunny.
9. A ball is round.
10. I like to sing.

Test 12
1. off
2. puff
3. cuff
4. doll
5. bell
6. hill
7. fall
8. toss
9. hiss
10. fuss

Test 13
1. back
2. pack
3. neck
4. peck
5. kick
6. sick
7. lock
8. dock
9. luck
10. suck

Test 14
1. bang
2. bank
3. king
4. song
5. sank
6. hang
7. ring
8. link
9. bunk
10. pink

Test 15
1. slip
2. slot
3. flat
4. flick
5. clap
6. clink
7. blot
8. black
9. glass
10. glad